A HELEN EXLEY GIFTBOOK

A Woman's Work is Never Done

PLANNER

Rowan Barnes-Murphy

D0364139

ADDRESSES, PHONE NUMBERS & E-MAIL ADDRESSES

'A woman's
work
is never done
– by men.'

GRAFFITO

'Kitchens,
broom closets and dust rags
are not in her dreams.'

COLEEN J. MCELROY, FROM "DAY HELP"

C

C

D

D

E

'If I ever get
to heaven,
I'll be stuck
making manna
in the
holy kitchens.'

JILL TWEEDIE (1936-1993)

'I would rather lie on a sofa
than sweep beneath it.'

SHIRLEY CONRAN, B.1932

'My mom is so busy
she has not got any hobbies. I suppose
her hobby is cleaning the house.'

CRAIG, AGE 9

H

'The fundamental
reason that women
do not achieve so greatly
as men is that women
have no wives.'

MARJORIE NICHOLSON

H

IJ

IJ

IJ

K

> 'Sometimes she pretends not to see me, when I behave very badly.'

FRASER
CAMILLE,
AGE 8

K

'One of my children wrote
in a third grade piece on how
her mother spent her time...
"one-half time on home,
one-half time on outside things,
one half-time writing.'"

CHARLOTTE MONTGOMERY

L

L

M

'I hate housework.
You make the beds,
    you do the dishes and
six months later you have to
start all over again.'

JOAN RIVERS, B.1933

M

👤	👤
🏠	🏠
📞	📞
📱	📱
💻	💻

'I gave up dreaming years ago.
All I do now is cook
and scrub and change my library book.'

SUE ARNOLD

NO

P

'Book tickets and a child needs to appear
as lead in the school play.
Get dressed for dinner
and a child is sick
on the living room carpet...'

PAM BROWN, B.1928

P

'Women want men, careers, money, children, friends, luxury, comfort, independence, freedom, respect, love and a three-dollar pantihose that won't run.'

PHYLLIS DILLER, B.1917

QR

'Mothers sometimes feel
like wearing a placard
"Everyone's buck stops here".'

PAM BROWN, B.1928

S

S

'To be today's real woman,
you need to have the
physique of Venus,
the cunning of Cleopatra,
the courage of Joan of Arc,
the wardrobe of Marie
Antoinette, and the cleaning
ability of Ammonia D.'

JOYCE JILLSON

S

T

T

'Children
should be
seen and not
smelt.'

JOYCE JILLSON

'The cock croweth
but the hen delivereth
the goods.'

AUTHOR UNKNOWN

'Just as every human being believes he has a novel in him, so every uxorious husband believes his wife has a cookery book in her.'

ALICE THOMAS ELLIS (1932-2005)

	_____			_____
🏠	_____		🏠	_____
	_____			_____
	_____			_____
📞	_____		📞	_____
📱	_____		📱	_____
💻	_____		💻	_____

'There's no pleasure
in having nothing to do.
The pleasure is
in having lots to do
and not doing it.'

MARY WILSON LITTLE

BIRTHDAYS AND SPECIAL EVENTS

1	2	3	4
5	6	7	8
9	10	11	12
13	14	15	16
17	18	19	20

21	22	23	24
25	26	27	28
29	30	31	

FEBRUARY

1	2	3	4
5	6	7	8
9	10	11	12
13	14	15	16
17	18	19	20

21	22
23	24
25	26
27	28/29

'Mothers never
get their Big Night Out.
Someone always
comes out in spots
ten minutes
before they leave.'

PAM BROWN, B.1928

MARCH

1	2	3	4
5	6	7	8
9	10	11	12
13	14	15	16
17	18	19	20

21	22	23	24
25	26	27	28
29	30	31	

'Life is too short
to stuff a mushroom.'

SHIRLEY CONRAN, B.1932,
FROM 'SUPERWOMAN'

1	2	3	4
5	6	7	8
9	10	11	12
13	14	15	16
17	18	19	20

21	22	23	24
25	26	27	28
29	30		

MAY

1	2	3	4
5	6	7	8
9	10	11	12
13	14	15	16
17	18	19	20

21	22	23	24
25	26	27	28
29	30	31	

JUNE

1	2	3	4
5	6	7	8
9	10	11	12
13	14	15	16
17	18	19	20

21	22	23	24
25	26	27	28
29	30		

'I can't see the point in
making tons of food if
people are just going to sit
there and eat it.'

JENNY ECLAIR

JULY

1	2	3	4
5	6	7	8
9	10	11	12
13	14	15	16
17	18	19	20

21	22	23	24
25	26	27	28
29	30	31	

AUGUST

1	2	3	4
5	6	7	8
9	10	11	12
13	14	15	16
17	18	19	20

21	22	23	24
25	26	27	28
29	30	31	

'Men never drip before getting
out of a shower. They saturate
themselves and then plunge
headlong into a towel
– leaving the bathroom as though
it's been through
a hard time in the North Sea.'

PAM BROWN, B.1928

SEPTEMBER

1	2	3	4
5	6	7	8
9	10	11	12
13	14	15	16
17	18	19	20

21	22	23	24
25	26	27	28
29	30		

Make Your Guest List

~~Bonjovi~~   ~~Billy Graham~~

Billy Bob
Mary Lou
Joe Ed
Betty Sue

OCTOBER

'Men live under the delusion that a gold ring makes a woman like making rounds of tea and cookies.'

PAM BROWN, B.1928

1	2	3	4
5	6	7	8
9	10	11	12
13	14	15	16

17	18	19	20
21	22	23	24
25	26	27	28
29	30		
31			

NOVEMBER

1	2	3	4
5	6	7	8
9	10	11	12
13	14	15	16
17	18	19	20

21	22	23	24
25	26	27	28
29	30		

'There comes a dreadful
moment in our lives
when foreign friends whom
we strongly urged to visit us
actually do so.'

VIRGINIA GRAHAM

DECEMBER

1	2	3	4
5	6	7	8
9	10	11	12
13	14	15	16
17	18	19	20

21	22	23	24
25	26	27	28
29	30	31	

GIFTS FOR ALL OCCASIONS

NAME	OCCASION	DATE

NAME	OCCASION	DATE

NAME	OCCASION	DATE

NAME	OCCASION	DATE

NAME	OCCASION	DATE

NAME	OCCASION	DATE

'We women ought
to put first things first.
Why should we
mind if men have
their faces on the money,
as long as we get
our hands on it?'

IVY BAKER PRIEST

NAME	OCCASION	DATE

NAME	OCCASION	DATE

NAME	OCCASION	DATE

NAME	OCCASION	DATE

'I like everyone saying
"That's just what I wanted"
and all the "oohs
and ahhhs"
and "you shouldn't haves".'

LESLEY GARNER, FROM "DAILY MAIL."

CHRISTMAS CARD LIST

NAME	YEAR	SENT	RECEIVED

NAME	YEAR	SENT	RECEIVED

NAME	YEAR	SENT	RECEIVED

NAME	YEAR	SENT	RECEIVED

NAME	YEAR	SENT	RECEIVED

'...one year there comes a point
when your average woman... faces the fact
that she has to do the whole damn thing over again....
She has to attend her work parties and his work parties
and the children's Christmas shows and carol services.
She has to remember cards
        and trees and decorations...
        as well as doing whatever she normally does....'

LESLEY GARNER, FROM "DAILY MAIL"

NAME	YEAR	SENT	RECEIVED

NAME	YEAR	SENT	RECEIVED

NAME	YEAR	SENT	RECEIVED

NAME	YEAR	SENT	RECEIVED

NAME	YEAR	SENT	RECEIVED

NAME	YEAR	SENT	RECEIVED

'We have won
the right to be
terminally
exhausted.'

ERICA JONG, B. 1942